Friends Who Sparkle Like the Stars
CoCo, Harry, Addie Mae, and Tucker

Carol Hair Moore

Illustrated by Michael Harrell

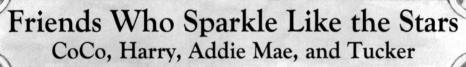

Friends Who Sparkle Like the Stars

To order any of Carol Moore's Children's books:
Marvin The Magnificent Nubian Goat
Busy Bumble Bee Rides The Waves
Ruby Kate's Scrumptious Tea Cake Party
Papa Mole's Secrets of Happiness
Friends Who Sparkle Like the Stars
Order online:
www.iwishyouicecreamandcake.com
www.amazon.com

Phone orders: (850) 893-1514
Series: I Wish You Ice Cream and Cake Book 5

Inquiries should be addressed to:
CyPress Publications
P.O. Box 2636
Tallahassee, Florida 32316-2636
http://cypresspublications.com
lraymond@nettally.com

Library of Congress Control Number: 2017949402

ISBN: 978-1-935083-52-8

First Edition

Printed in the United States of America

Introduction

CoCo, Harry, Addie Mae, and Tucker are four friends who live on Moore Farm. These four friends are very different from each other and yet are alike in many ways. Discover what it takes to be a friend and what makes friendship special by reading about these animal friends. The fifth volume in Carol Moore's informative and engaging series of children's books, Friends Who Sparkle Like the Stars, helps us learn differences make friendships rewarding. The four friends in this book are different in many ways but alike in the traits that matter most: love, kindness, sincerity, and support. The beautiful detailed paintings by award-winning artist Michael Harrell capture the attention of adults and children of all ages. Young children will enjoy listening to the story and searching through the beautifully illustrated pages for the four friends. Beginning readers will identify with the characters and the friendships they make at the farm. Adults and children will learn about some of the animals, insects and plants of North Florida from the Education Pages of this book.

~Sunny Saunders, Coordinator of Consumer Education and Family Engagement, Office of Early Learning, Florida Department of Education

Sunny Saunders retired from the Leon County public school system after 40 years working as a teacher, literacy coach and professional development trainer. She has taught pre-service teachers for Florida State University, Flagler College and Santa Fe College. She served on the boards of the Leon County Reading Council and the National Board Certified Teachers of Leon County and was a past-president of each organization. Currently, she is the Coordinator of Consumer Education and Family Engagement for the Office of Early Learning, Florida Department of Education.

Dedicated to Edgar Murray Moore, Sr.
"I would not wish any companion in the world but you."
Shakespeare - *The Tempest*.

It was an especially pretty day at Moore Farm. The wind was whistling through the trees.

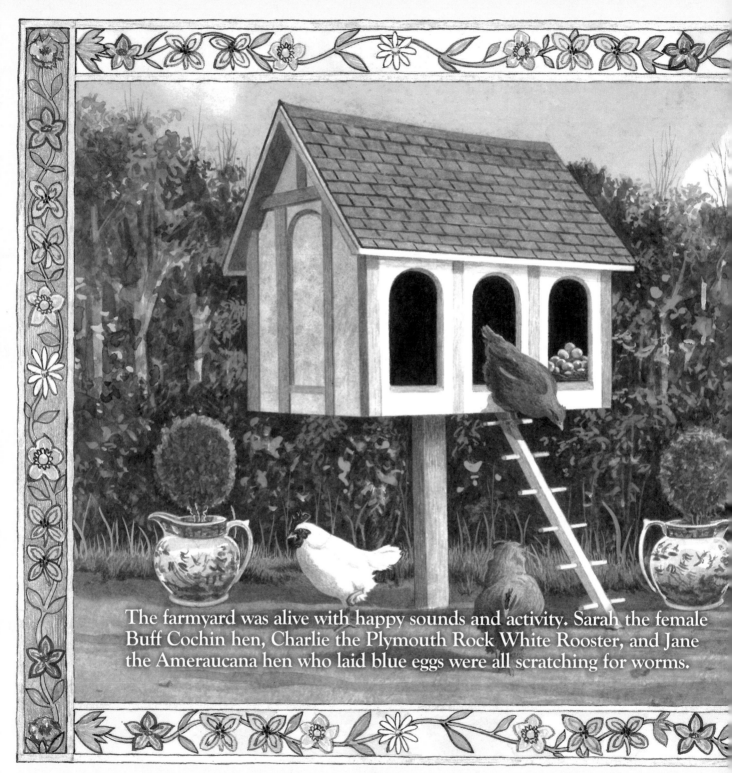

The farmyard was alive with happy sounds and activity. Sarah the female Buff Cochin hen, Charlie the Plymouth Rock White Rooster, and Jane the Ameraucana hen who laid blue eggs were all scratching for worms.

Marvin the Nubian goat was playing with the red, white, and black fuzzy kittens. They were enjoying the warm sunshine.

CoCo the small black and white Maltipoo dog, and Harry the fluffy grey Himalayan cat went over to the old wire fence that was covered with pink Old Blush China Roses.

The two friends met their good friend Addie Mae. Addie Mae was a shiny
Black Angus cow who was expecting a calf very soon.

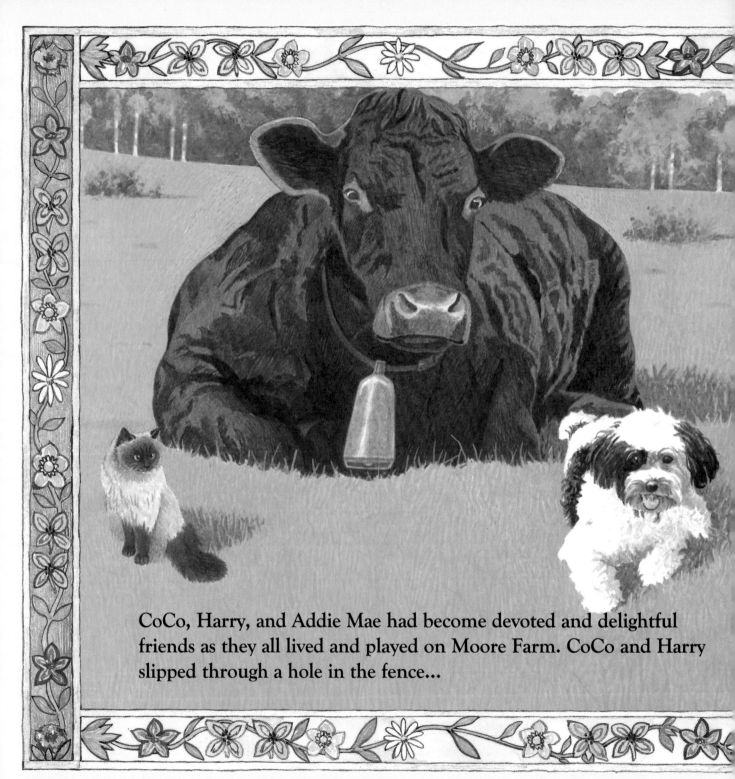

CoCo, Harry, and Addie Mae had become devoted and delightful
friends as they all lived and played on Moore Farm. CoCo and Harry
slipped through a hole in the fence...

. . . and away the three ran through the pasture to the fish pond. Addie Mae was very large with her unborn calf. Coco and Harry ran ahead of her.

The Crimson Clover was wet with dew. The sun made it sparkle like a field of rubies.

The pond was full of fish jumping in the cool water. Crickets were singing and the green frogs were leaping on the lily pads.

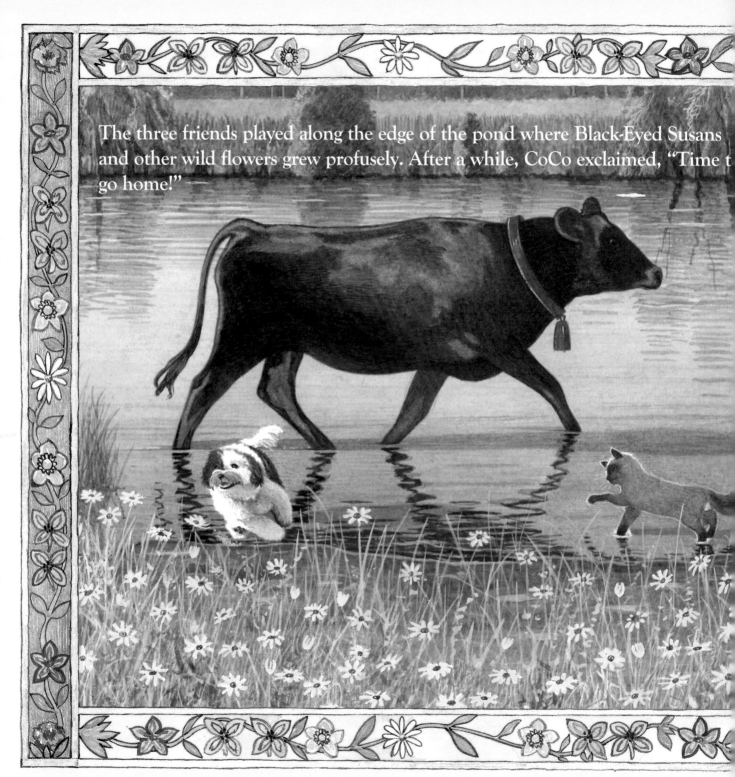

The three friends played along the edge of the pond where Black-Eyed Susans and other wild flowers grew profusely. After a while, CoCo exclaimed, "Time to go home!"

CoCo looked at her two friends and thought, "How different we are, and yet we are friends who care about each other and enjoy being together!"

CoCo discovered four wonderful things that day. "No matter how small or large you are, no matter the color of your hair or skin, no matter where you live, in a grand house or a red barn—if your heart is loving and kind you can be a devoted and delightful friend."

CoCo and Harry went to the big white house. Addie Mae went to the red barn. Addie Mae's calf was born that night as she lay in a bed of soft hay.

The new calf was named Tucker. Addie Mae was an attentive and loving mother. She whispered to her baby, "I love you."

Tucker was a fine Black Angus calf who stood for the first time with wobbly knees.

15

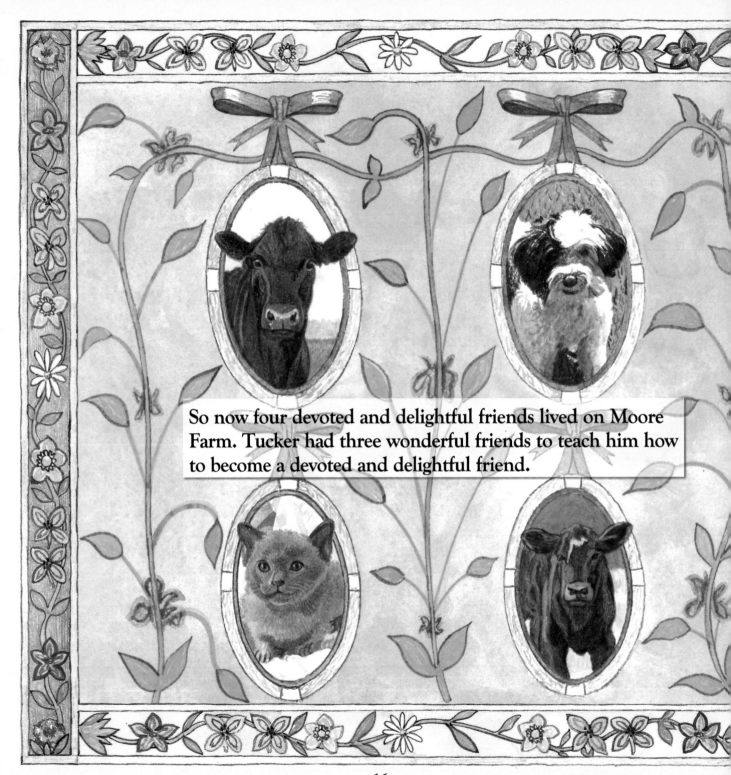

So now four devoted and delightful friends lived on Moore Farm. Tucker had three wonderful friends to teach him how to become a devoted and delightful friend.

Devoted and delightful friends bring joy and happiness to themselves and others.

Their sincerity brings laughter instead of tears.

Their companionship takes loneliness away.

Their support brings understanding rather than confusion.

Let's all be devoted and delightful friends. Let's sparkle like the stars each day in every way.

Education Pages

Ameraucana

Ameraucana hens lay blue eggs. They were bred in the United States from Araucana chickens brought from Chile. True Ameraucanas are not very common and are often confused with Americanas and Easter Eggers, which is not a recognized breed but also lays a blue egg. Ameraucanas are hardy and sweet with males weighing around 6 pounds and females 5 pounds. American Standard of Perfection recognizes eight color variants: black, blue, blue wheaten, brown red, buff, silver, wheaten, and white.

American Green Frog

A medium-sized frog (up to 2.5 in long) in some shade of green ranging from bright yellowish-olive to lime green. The color can change depending on lighting and temperature. They have smooth skin and large toe pads and range from Delaware to Southeast Florida and west to Central Texas. Most often found in small ponds, large lakes, marshes and streams, they prefer habitats with plentiful floating vegetation. Males call from, and will defend, their territory. The call sounds like a plucked banjo string, usually as a single note. Calling is more prevalent, as is breeding, immediately after rainfall. Offspring are tadpoles, which may metamorphose (change to frogs) during the same breeding season or may overwinter until the next summer. An insectivore, the frog usually consumes flies, mosquitoes, and other small insects.

Angus Cow

Native to the counties of Aberdeen and Angus in Scotland, it is known in much of the world as the Aberdeen-Angus and is one of the three breeds of polled cattle in the United Kingdom. "Polled" refers to an animal without horns in a species that normally carries horns. A likeness of polled cattle appears in prehistoric drawings in caves in Aberdeen and Angus, Scotland. First introduced into the U.S. in 1873, the Angus is one of the most successful breeds of beef cattle in the United States. "100% Angus" is a ubiquitous and respected marketing slogan. Angus are docile, hardy, and cows calve easily. Angus cows weigh about 1212 pounds and bulls about 1874 pounds. Cows are considered to have excellent mothering abilities. Calves are produced at an early age (24-27 months). With a gestation period of 9 months, cows produce one calf per year. Calves are weaned after 8-10 months.

Black-Eyed Susan

Found in all 48 contiguous states, the Black-Eyed Susan is one of America's favorite wildflowers. A sunflower plant native to North America, it blooms in late summer and early autumn with yellow ray florets circling a brown or black dome-shaped cone (the eye) of many small disc florets. Breeding has produced a range of additional colors. This is the gorgeous gold wildflower growing on its own in great sheets of riotous color along highways or in abandoned fields. Who was Susan for whom the flower is named? Nobody knows, but legend says the name comes from an Old English poem by John Gay, called "Black-Eyed Susan."

All in the downs, the fleet was moored,
Banners waving in the wind.
When Black-Eyed Susan came aboard,
And eyed the burly men.
"Tell me ye sailors, tell me true
Does my Sweet William sail with you?"

The plant is also a traditional Native American medicinal herb used for colds, flu, infection, swelling, and snake bite (not all parts are edible). It is also known to be toxic to cats when ingested.

Buff Cochin Hen

Originally bred in China, Cochins were exported to the U.S. and Britain in the middle 1800s. "Buff" refers to the variety having a soft golden color. Other varieties include Black, Blue, Partridge, Silver Laced, Golden Laced, Splash, and White. Importation of the distinctive and beautiful Cochin chickens into the U.S. is often credited with creating the "poultry fancy" or craze for exotic breeds that swept the country in the 1940s and '50s. One source states, "It is doubtful that any other single breed of chicken has inspired more people to poultry as a hobby or fancy." They are one of the largest chickens with cocks (males) weighing up to 11 pounds; however, their most distinctive and appealing feature is their soft and abundant plumage, which makes them seem even larger. Their plumage extends to cover leg and foot. Eggs are light brown and standard sized. Cochins are tame, quiet, and calm, regarded as good mothers and foster mothers. The Cochin hens are considered the best fowls for hatching and brooding ducks and turkeys. Extremely hardy, they thrive in conditions where other breeds might perish.

Calf

A calf (plural calves) is the young of domestic cattle. Calf is the term used from birth to weaning. Born after 9 months, calves usually stand within minutes of calving and suckle within an hour. Since for a few days they are unable to keep up with the rest of the herd, mothers will sometimes hide their calves, returning several times a day to suckle them. After about a week, calves are able to keep up with the herd. Calves are usually weaned at 8-9 months. A bull calf will gain about 75 pounds per month.

Cricket

Crickets are small-to medium-sized insects, distantly related to the grasshopper, with mostly cylindrical somewhat flattened bodies. There are more than 900 species of crickets worldwide. They come in all shapes and sizes. The largest, the bull cricket, is 2 inches long. Some can fly, while others have no wings. Mainly nocturnal, crickets are perhaps best known for their chirping. Chirping is the loud persistent song of males trying to attract females. (Some species are mute.) Females lack the necessary adaptations and do not chirp. Crickets can be found in many habitats. Some live in the upper tree canopy, others in bushes and grasses, and still others on or in the ground. Folklore and mythology surrounding crickets is extensive. In some cultures, the singing of crickets may signal rain or even a financial windfall. In Cabeza de Vaca's chronicle of his ill-fated journey across the southeast, including North Florida in the 1500s, the sudden chirping of crickets signaled the sighting of land just as he and his crew were running out of water. Crickets have been major characters in books and novels, from Charles Dickens's, *The Cricket on the Hearth*, Collodi's *The Adventures of Pinocchio*, and Selden's *The Cricket in Times Square* to name a few. Crickets are a major source of food in some parts of the world. In Thailand, there are 20,000 farmers raising crickets. The food conversion rate of crickets is 5 times that for beef cattle.

Crimson Clover

A winter or summer annual ground cover, it is most often seen in early spring in the Southeast but is also gaining popularity as a summer legume in colder regions. Rapid, robust growth provides early spring nitrogen for full season crops and functions as a weed suppressing green manure. Legumes such as crimson clover obtain nitrogen from the air and can provide as much nitrogen as is obtained from 100-150 pounds of fertilizer per acre. It is a staple forage crop in the southeast and is often seen as a roadside cover. The leaves and stems of crimson clover resemble those of red clover. Florets are a bright crimson color and open in succession from the bottom to the top. They produce abundant nectar and are visited by various types of bees. It will grow in soils of poor quality and thrives in well-drained sandy and clayey soils.

Hay

Hay comes in many forms. It is literally a grass, legume, or other herbaceous plant that has been cut, dried, and stored for animal fodder, particularly for grazing animals such as cattle, horses, goats and sheep. Since it can be stored, hay can be used when there is insufficient pasture on which to graze an animal or when grazing is unavailable due to season, weather, or confinement. Many varieties of plants are suitable for hay production: Bermuda, alfalfa, clover, and sometimes oats, barley, and wheat. Different types of animals require different hay, but the right hay can provide 100% of the diet for grazing animals. Cattle and horses digest hay using different mechanisms and require differing feeding techniques. Horses digest food in small amounts while on the move. Cattle on the other hand use their four-chambered stomachs and a process called rumination to take a considerable amount of time to digest hay, even while lying down. Hay must be cut, dried, and stored at the proper times. If hay is baled too moist, there is a significant danger of spontaneous combustion. Early hay balers, some still in use today, produce bales weighing approximately 75 pounds. Those bales could be moved and stored by hand. Balers now produce bales weighing up to 3,000 pounds and must be handled by large tractors. There are many different storage solutions for hay: barns, haystacks of various configurations, open storage, wrapped bales, etc. Hay is one of the safest feeds to provide to domesticated grazing herbivores.

Himalayan Cat

Also called Himalayan Persian, or Colourpoint Persian (Europe), it is a long-haired cat identical in type to the Persian with exception of its blue eyes and point coloration resulting from crossing the Persian with the Siamese. The Cat Fanciers' Association considers the Himalayan as a color variation of the Persian, although some of the early cats were bred with more Siamese traits. The different colors are exhibited primarily on the "points": face mask, ears, tail, and legs. The bulk of the fur on the body is white or cream, but points come in many colors. Males may weigh 12 pounds and because of their massive coats may appear much larger. Good companions, they are intelligent and very social with a playful side. They crave affection and love to be petted and groomed.

Lily Pads

Round, flat, and waxy with a flower (usually white), lily pads are a water lily plant sometimes referred to as the lotus flower. Beautiful flowers bloom on top of the leaves, which appear to be floating on the surface of the water; however, the roots of the plant are attached to the bed of the water body. Oxygen is provided to the roots by the hollow stem extending from the leaf through the water column to the roots. Growing in the calm shoreline waters of lakes and ponds, lily pads benefit their habitat by providing shelter for fish, shade and oxygen for fish to breathe. They can, however, become invasive and dominate a water body having a depth of 6 feet or less. The beautiful nature of lily pads has led to their widespread use as ornamental plants, which enhances the opportunity for invasion. Native Americans used parts of the lily pad or water lily for medicinal purposes. Roots were mashed to create a poultice for swelling; the pads were used as cooling compresses and other parts of the plant for aids in digestion and as a mouth rinse.

Maltipoo

Maltipoos are a cross-breed, or hybrid, dog obtained by breeding a Maltese and a Toy or Miniature Poodle. Like their parents, Maltipoos are affectionate and gentle and like nothing more than to cuddle in their owner's lap. They make great companions and therapy dogs. Weighing between 5 and 15 pounds, they come in a variety of colors. Many are bicolor with a mixture of white and another color. They have medium to long soft coats and shed little or not at all. Fun-loving and feisty, Maltipoos enjoy games, walks, and most of all just being with their people. Being companion dogs, they may suffer separation anxiety if frequently left alone for long periods. They will alert-bark when they see something or someone out of the ordinary. Maltipoos have an average lifespan of 12 years, but many live to be 14-16 years old.

Nubian Goat

Sometimes referred to as the Anglo-Nubian goat, but in the United States usually simply the Nubian goat, it was developed in Great Britain from the Old English Milch Goat and Nubian bucks imported from India, Russia, and Egypt. Known for their large, pendulous ears and Roman nose, males weigh approximately 175 pounds and females 135. Their hair is short, fine, and glossy. Markings can be any color or combination of colors. Nubians are sociable, outgoing, and vocal. They readily attach to their owners and will often call for their owner. Normally Nubians are kept hornless by disbudding within approximately two weeks of birth. It is primarily a milk goat with very high butterfat content; however, some producers use them for meat production.

Plymouth Rock

Until the early 1940s the Plymouth Rock was the most widespread chicken breed in the United States. It was used to develop broiler hybrids on industrial chicken farms and declined in popularity as a domestic fowl. The number of Rocks is now increasing. The original and most commonly recognized variety is the Barred Rock, distinguished by the black and white patterns that produce lines or bars in their feathers. The White variety is among six other popular colors. Rocks are raised both for their meat and eggs. Large and heavy with a bright red comb and wattles and yellow un-feathered legs, they are beautiful birds. Males typically weigh approximately 7.5 pounds. Smart, friendly, and happy to be handled, they make good pets.

Stars

Stars have captured our imagination, curiosity, and study ever since we humans stood erect and gazed to the heavens. Understanding of our celestial neighbors has progressed, regressed, and moved forward in quantum leaps in recent decades. What are these amazing sparkling points of light in our night sky? A star is a luminous sphere of plasma held together by its own gravity. For a portion of its life (the part most important to us) a star shines due to thermonuclear fusion of hydrogen into helium in its core, releasing energy that traverses the star's interior and then radiates into space. Our nearest and most familiar star is the Sun. We see uncountable stars in the night sky of our galaxy, the Milky Way, but most of the stars in the Universe are invisible to us and to our most powerful telescopes. Stars are not spread uniformly across the Universe, but are normally grouped in galaxies along with interstellar gas and dust. A typical galaxy contains hundreds of billions of stars, and there are more than 100 billion galaxies in the observable universe. This does not include the portions of the Universe we cannot see, which may be, and is likely, much larger than what we can see. The nearest star to the Earth, apart from the Sun, is Proxima Centauri, which is 4.2 light-years away. Traveling at the speed of the space shuttle, 30,000 mph, it would take about 150,000 years to arrive at Proxima Centauri. Due to their great distance from Earth, stars other than the Sun appear to twinkle because of the effects of the Earth's atmosphere. Used in religious practices and for navigation and orientation, stars have been important to civilizations throughout the history of the world.

Worms

Worms are animals that have long tube-like bodies and no limbs. They vary in size from microscopic to over 190 feet (a marine variety). Worms have no arms, legs, or eyes. Worms that live inside other animals are parasitic worms, others are free-living worms and come in many forms. The most readily recognized is the earthworm. There are over 2500 different kinds of earthworms. In one acre of land there can be over one million earthworms. They live where there is food, oxygen, and favorable temperatures. Earthworms have the ability to replace or replicate lost segments (portions of their body), some more easily than others. A tail may be easy to replace, but a head may be much more difficult. Earthworms tunnel deeply in the soil and mix the subsoil with the topsoil. A secretion of the earthworm contains nitrogen, which is an important nutrient for plants. Baby worms are hatched from a cocoon smaller than a grain of rice. Although worms don't have eyes, they can sense light and will move away from a light source. Charles Darwin spent 39 years studying earthworms.

Author Carol Hair Moore

Carol's warm and loving story of her animal friends' relationships reflects her life-long love of animals and her years of living on a farm. She spent her early years on a farm and later raised her family in the country with the animal friends, and others, presented in this story. In this and all of her books, she seeks to instill in her readers a desire to be kind and faithful and to treat others like you want to be treated.

With a B.S. in Elementary Education from Florida State University, Carol taught second grade and now spends her time with school visits, book festivals and caring for her loving family. This is her fifth published book, all illustrated by nationally known artist, Michael Harrell.

Carol lives in Tallahassee, Florida with her retired attorney husband, Edgar Murray Moore, Sr. They have three married children, six grandsons and one granddaughter.

Of her passion for writing children's books, Carol says, "If I have encouraged children in some small way to be loving, honest, kind, and to treat others with compassion, then I have done what God has guided me to do."

Illustrator Michael Harrell

Michael Harrell is a native of Tallahassee, Florida. He received a B.F.A. from the University of Georgia in 1989.

Harrell's seascapes and landscapes paintings can be found in private and corporate collections throughout the U.S. and abroad.

His oils and watercolors have been featured in many national publications, including *American Artist Watercolor* magazine, *American Art Collector*, and *The Artist's Magazine*. More than a dozen top galleries represent Harrell's work and, in 2004, The *Artist's Magazine* listed Michael Harrell as one of the top 20 artists in the United States to watch.

Michael Harrell's clients have included American Express, Paramount Pictures, Seaside, and the Mystic Seaport Museum.

Michael is represented by The Gallery On Greene, Key West, Morris & Whiteside Galleries in Hilton Head, and The Sylvan Gallery in Charleston.

Sparkle like the Stars ~ Shine like the Moon
Be Warm like the Sun